AN OXFORD
QUIZ BOOK

*For what purpose was this strangely shaped
building originally used?*

Julia Owen

S. B. Publications

By the same author
The Secret Cotswolds
The Gloucestershire Quiz Book

First published in 1997 by S. B. Publications,
c/o 19 Grove Road, Seaford, East Sussex BN25 1TP

ISBN 1 85770 140 2

Designed and typeset by CGB, Lewes
Printed by Island Press
3 Cradle Hill Industrial Estate, Seaford, East Sussex BN25 3JE
Tel: 01323 490222

CONTENTS

COVER QUESTIONS

Front: For what purpose was this building used, and where is it?

Back: Who was the maker of this turret clock, and where is it?

INTRODUCTION

QUIZZES are firmly back in fashion – although they never really went out of fashion for people have always loved to test their knowledge and stump their friends. Radio quizzes like *Brain of Britain* and the *Round Britain Quiz*, now in its twenty-fifth year, have enduringly faithful audiences.

Television has produced ratings-busting contests like *Mastermind* with all the drama of the black swivel chair and interrogation room lighting, and a new edition of *University Challenge* has inexhaustable teams of brilliant young students pitting their wits against formidable contestants from all over the country.

The other kinds of quiz are of a more informal nature. Everyone likes to puzzle over Christmas quizzes set by newspapers, sporting quizzes linked to top events, or family quizzes which jog nostalgic memories. Pubs are packed when they hold Quiz Evenings; teenagers reach for their *Trivial Pursuit* cards; teachers of small children make learning fun with question and answer sessions. And perhaps that is the key to the enduring appeal of the quiz for it stretches the brain in a very pleasurable way.

Many quiz questions naturally focus on the world directly around us – the countryside, the towns, the county. This book is devoted to the countryside, the towns and the county of Oxfordshire – one of the most beautiful parts of Britain. Its residents are rightly proud of its 800 years of history, and are keen to learn more. These questions may prompt their curiosity to seek further information and the answers may well provide it.

The questions fall into natural categories. Some may require specialist knowledge in certain areas, others just a need to know a bit about everything. Hopefully there will be something here for everyone.

Julia Owen
Autumn 1997

1 ALFRED

900. Alfred, son of Aethelwulf, passed away, six days before All Saints' Day. He was king over all the English, except for that part which was under Danish rule; and held his kingdom for one and a half years less than thirty.

The Anglo-Saxon Chronicles

1 Name the rival kingdoms spanning Oxfordshire in King Alfred's day.

2 Alfred's birthplace, and while we are about it, the year of his birth.

3 The Blowing Stone came to rest in the front garden of a cottage in Kingston Lisle after being dislodged from the top of White Horse Hill by high-spirited university students. What is it? And what is the legend connecting it to King Alfred?

4 'Alfred had me made' or in Anglo-Saxon, *Aelfred mec heht Gewyrcan*. Thus runs the inscription on one of the jewels in the Ashmoleon Museum. What is it called and where was it found.

5 Who was the model for the lifesize statue of King Alfred erected in the market place at Wantage in 1877?

6 And who was the sculptor of the said statue.

7 At Wantage there is an Alfred's Well. But which Alfred?

8 And Alfred's Castle? Like the White Horse, probably of Iron Age origin. Again, which Alfred?

9 The White Horse carved in the chalk downs above Uffington has its origins in the mists of time. One legend links it to Alfred's famous victory over the Danes in 871. Where?

10 Its name in Anglo-Saxon meant 'fern-covered hill'. Alfred had a royal manor here.

2 ALICE

*Curtsey while you're thinking what to say.
It saves time.*

Lewis Carroll. *Through the Looking Glass*

1 The creator of *Alice in Wonderland* was mathematics tutor at which Oxford college?

2 Who was Alice?

3 What was Lewis Carroll's real name?

4 Folly Bridge was the starting point of the river excursion in 1892 which inspired the famous children's stories. What was the destination?

5 The *Pool of Tears* episode was based on a real event. Which one?

6 Alice bought her barley sugar here, and Carroll immortalised it as the Sheep Shop in *Alice Through the Looking Glass.*

7 Carroll wrote of seeing fields looking like squares on a chessboard. What was the view?

8 Queen Victoria enjoyed Alice in Wonderland so much that the author promised, and did, send her a copy of his next work. What was its title?

9 Lewis Carroll did his own illustrations for the book until persuaded by his publisher to enlist professional help. Who was the artist?

10 And what was the book's original title?

3 ALL CREATURES GREAT AND SMALL

The griffine, bustard, turkey and capon,
Lett other hungry mortalls gape on
And on their ones with stomacks fall hard
but lett All Souls men have the mallard.

The *Mallard Song* for All Souls' Night;
All Souls College, Oxford.

1 The white rhino's Oxfordshire habitat?

2 A moving epitaph to 'Ringwood, an OTTER-HOUND of extraordinary Sagacity' can be seen by the Octagonal Pond of this stately home.

3 On these 4,000 acres of low-lying marshy countryside there were bitter riots in the nineteenth century when landowners tried to enclose and drain them. Now the area is a paradise for wildlife. Name it?

4 Where might you see a donkey wheel?

5 What is the gruesome paving material used at Wantage? It's to do with sheep. . .

6 The Yellow Brimstone is usually the first to emerge here each spring - but thirty of the fifty-six species of British butterfly can be spotted in this 250 acre nature reserve.

7 Doves were always on the menu at this now ruined medieval house which has the finest, circular dovecot in the country.

8 Davey Barnard's extraordinary gravestone takes the form of a marble five-barred stable gate with a horse's head peeping out of a marble horseshoe, perfectly reflecting his lifelong passion for horses. Where does it stand?

9 *Vermis sum.* This epitaph on his tomb in Burford church is said to have been chosen by William Lenthall, Speaker of the House of Commons during the Long Parliament, as acknowledgement of the mistakes of his political career. To what creature does the inscription refer?

10 Where can you see an eighteenth century duck decoy, and ducks?

4 ARTS AND CRAFTS

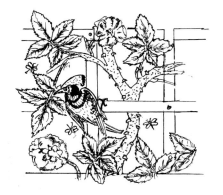

The wind's on the wold
And the night is a-cold,
And Thames runs chill
'Twixt mead and hill.
But kind and dear
Is the old house here
William Morris

1 Dante Gabriel Rossetti called it the 'doziest of old grey beehives', William Morris chose it as the destination of the narrator in his Utopian fantasy *News From Nowhere*, and lived there.

2 This Slade Professor of Fine Arts managed to persuade a team of undergraduates, including Oscar Wilde of all people, to do a spot of road mending at North Hinksey to remind them of 'the pleasures of useful muscular work'.

3 Whose dreamlike paintings of the *Legend of the Briar Rose* adorn the walls of the saloon in Buscot Park near Faringdon?

4 Name the little church near Woodcote which has a memorial window by glass engraver Laurence Whistler dedicated to artist Eric Kennington.

5 Where is there a trail of contemporary sculpture through ancient woodland.

6 It was all a bit of a disaster. The plaster was not properly prepared and the frescoes barely survive, but a group of young Pre-Raphaelite artists completed this monumental Oxford decorating scheme in 1857.

7 Where can you see Edward Burne-Jone's magnificent stained glass window celebrating the life of St Frideswide?

8 The Oxfordshire Craft Guild displays its work in a theatre. Which one?

9 Renowned sculptor of the memorial to Lady Ottoline Morrell, 1920s literary hostess and *grande dame* of Garsington Manor.

10 William Morris described this great medieval barn near Kelmscott, built by the monks of Beaulieu Abbey, as 'noble as a cathedral'.

5 CHURCHES

1 The residents of this market town blew up their medieval minster with gunpowder in 1792 rather than pay for repairs to it.

2 Five generations of the Fettiplace family are buried in this lovely rural church. Two spectacular seventeenth century triple-decker tombs have life-size effigies of their occupants reclining on their elbows as if on bunk beds.

3 The clock on the tower of this church has only one hand.

4 Surely the grandest Methodist church in the county, but not originally built as a house of God.

5 The remains of Saint Egburg were transferred to this village church from Bicester Abbey at the Dissolution.

6 Among the splendid monuments in this large church is one to a certain Geoffrey Dormer, his wife and his twenty-five children.

7 The Royal Chapel and stables are all that remain of a fine estate.

8 Oliver Cromwell heavy handedly put down a potential rebellion among his troops by imprisoning 340 of the so-called Levellers in this church. One scratched his name on the font: 'Anthony Sedley 1649 – Prisner' Next morning Cromwell had the ringleaders shot.

9 A fine series of wall paintings dating from the thirteenth century were discovered by the vicar of this church in 1866. He went to London to procure 'a wash with which to fix them', returning to find his curate had decided to whitewash them over again.

10 Surely the most extraordinary stained glass window in the county – it features Christ's family tree, starting with Jesse. Where is it?

6 COUNTRY HOUSES

*Thanks sir, cried I, 'tis
very fine,
But where d'ye sleep, or
where d'ye dine?
I find, by all you have
been telling,
That 'tis a house, but not
a dwelling.*
Alexander Pope.

1 It stands in grounds of more than 2,000 acres; the house and courtyards alone cover seven acres. Definitely a palace rather than a rural retreat.

2 Whose family home was Sulgrave Manor, near Banbury?

3 Roosevelt and Churchill held talks here during the war, now it is a conference centre.

4 Toad Hall? A grand house with an unusual chapel in Strawberry Hill Gothic style.

5 Ardington House has an imperial staircase. Describe an imperial staircase

6 A Jacobean jewel with explosive connections.

7 A ghostly ruined manor house in the Windrush valley.

8 This grand house with a strong Catholic tradition belonged to the same family for more than 800 years. It also had a prehistoric stone circle which has now been re-created within the grounds.

9 Marvellous medieval manor house with moat, drawbridge and gate house owned by Lord Saye and Sele.

10 This exquisite 'doll's house' on the Wiltshire side of the Vale of the White Horse is owned by National Trust.

7 ECCENTRICS

England is the paradise of individuality, eccentricity, heresy, anomalies, hobbies and humours.

George Santayana. *Soliloquies in England.*

1 Villagers thought he was quite mad and were probably grateful he stopped short of turning this Oxfordshire village into anotherPortmeiron.

2 The second Lord Faringdon enlisted the help of a Mexician- inpired muralist to celebrate the achievements of socialism – where?

3 This aristocratic lady, who is buried in a simple grave at Swinbrook, cultivated some very strange friendships. But then she had a husband who held very strange views.

4 Who was described as 'the greatest epicure of his day'. He lived in a castle, of course.

5 His collection has been described as 'an overcrowded combination of Aladdin's cave, art gallery and superior junk shop'. By 1884, when he gave it to the university, he had already amassed 15,000 bizarre items.

6 This Victorian poet was sent down from Trinity for taking pot shots out of his window.

7 It was designed to be 'entirely useless' – all 140 feet of it.

8 He was not only one of the richest men in Britain but also the most generous. During his lifetime he gave away more than £20 million.

9 He rode his first winner at the age of eight, and was still racing at the advanced age of seventy-four.

10 Sir Francis Page, the 'Hanging Judge' who sentenced more than 100 men to death, was born in Bloxham, but lived and died here in 1741.

8 FAMOUS MEN AND WOMEN

And what is fame? The meanest have their day,
The greatest can but blaze, and pass away.

Alexander Pope. *Satires*
and Epistles.

1 Who was born on 30 November 1874 at Blenheim Palace?

2 This distinguished and self taught mathematician gave her name to one of Oxford's first colleges for women.

3 The patron saint of Oxford.

4 Name the British Prime Minister buried at Sutton Courtenay.

5 Name the 'Oxford Martyrs'.

6 A very famous American (1968) Rhodes Scholar.

7 Two famous Oxfordshire men who shared the same name. One gave his name to a kind of car, the other, a writer and artist, was a leading figure in the Arts and Crafts movement.

8 Who was 'the Fair Rosamund'?

9 He was sixty two years at New College, and Warden from 1903 to 1924. He gave his name to comical linguistic justapositions, typically – to his undergraduates: 'You have tasted a whole worm. You have hissed my mystery lectures. You will leave by the town drain'. His students adored him.

10 Who was the founder of the exclusive public school at Radley.

9 FILM LOCATIONS

For years I have been known for saying 'include me out'; but today I'm giving it up for ever.
Samuel Goldwyn in an address at Balliol in March 1945.

LOOK closely at some of our best loved British films and tv serials, and there in the background you will see the real star of the show – Oxfordshire. Can you match these films to their locations?

1 Gilded youth at Oxford. Evelyn Waugh's famous novel made an even more famous tv serialisation starring Jeremy Irons.

2 C S Lewis, the Christian writer, is perhaps better known for his childrens' stories, *Chronicles of Narnia.* This moving film of his relationship with an American woman dying of cancer unfolds against a backdrop of academic life in post-war Oxford.

3 Warner Brothers transformed the courtyard of this stately home into a convincing replica of London's Covent Garden for a new film version of *Black Beauty*

4 Helena Bonham Carter, Vanessa Redgrave and Anthony Hopkins starred in this adaptation of E M Forster's famous novel, partly filmed at Peppard Common near Henley on Thames.

5 *The Madness of King George* (1995) was filmed partly on location at Thame Park. Who played King George?

6 The old magistrates court at Oxford's Town Hall provided a sober location for court scenes in John Cleese's hilarious comedy about crime.

7 No one has put modern Oxford on the map like this well known tv detective with a taste for opera and real ale.

8 This was a musical setting for *Carrington,* the 1995 film about the Bloomsbury Group with Emma Thompson in the title role.

9 This fine moated medieval castle is one of the unlikely settings for the American 1990 comedy *Three Men and a Little Lady*, sequel to *Three Men and a Baby*, both starring Tom Selleck.

10 This picturesque Oxfordshire village has featured in the BBC's *Just William* series, Rowan Atkinson's hilarious wedding commercial, and the adaptation of Joanna Trollope's *A Village Affair* for ITV.

10 FOOD AND DRINK

Oxfordshire claims but one homemade dish – boiled bacon set upon boiled cabbage.

1 Whose tin of Oxford Marmalade was recovered from the ill-fated expedition to the Antarctic? And where is it now?

2 The Great Kitchen is the glory of this medieval manor house.

3 Oxfordshire town boasting a strange ancient custom whereby visiting monarchs threw buns to the hungry populace waiting beneath the Town Hall windows.

4 Although better known for wool, this delightful town has a famous seventeenth century Butter Cross.

5 What is 'Old Hookey'?

6 Where can you see Lewis Carroll's famous 'Treacle Well'?

7 Whatever the season, one of Britain's finest country restaurants. . .

8 The Christmas Feast of the Boar's Head at Queen's College is held to commemorate a bizarre incident in Shotover Forest. A student reportedly saved himself from certain death by shoving a volume of which classical author into the jaws of an enraged wild boar?

9 It is highly prized by the London markets and grows wild in the chalk streams in the Vale of the White Horse.

10 Usually poached (but not eggs). This was the traditional fare of Wychwood Forest.

11 GARDENS

I know a little garden close
Set thick with lily and red rose,
Where I would wander if
I might
From dewy dawn to dewy
night . . .
William Morris.
The Life and Death of Jason.

1   He founded the Oxford Botannic Garden in 1621.

2   The basis of which famous collection was formed by a 'cabinet of
    rarities' given by the son of Charles I's gardener, John Tradescant. He
    had acquired them on his plant hunting expeditions.

3   The gardens of this house boast a splendid Archbishop's Maze.

4   This Anglo-American garden has a tree planted in memory of President
    Kennedy.

5   Harold Peto created an elegant water garden linking this fine eighteenth
    century house to its lake.

6   Designer of the park at Blenheim – and one of Britain's most famous
    landscape architects.

7   Where can you find Oxford University's Arboretum? Not in Oxford. . .

8   The most complete surviving example of the work of William Kent –
    complete with Pyramid House, Temple of Echo, cascades and pools.

9   This garden was set up in 1932 at a cost of £350. Its founder intended it
    to be a training school for female professional and amateur gardeners.

10 Where can you see a replica of Queen Mary's rose garden?

12 LITERARY LIVES

*Particularly against books the Home Secretary is.
If we can't stamp out literature in the country, we
can at least stop it being brought in from outside.*

Evelyn Waugh. *Vile Bodies.*

1 Who wrote the classic Oxford novel *Zuleika Dobson,* first published in 1911.

2 Where can you see 'Pope's Tower'? Alexander Pope completed his verse translation of Homer's *Iliad* in the top rooms of the tower in 1718.

3 Famous literary family who lived at Swinbrook. Five sisters.

4 Prestigious Oxford poetry prize awarded annually since 1806.

5 The school room in the tiny village of Uffington at the foot of the White Horse downs has a small museum dedicated to one of its famous literary inhabitants.

6 Name the other.

7 'That sweet city with her dreaming spires' is endlessly quoted. But who wrote those famous lines about Oxford?

8 *Three Men in a Boat* celebrates a hilarious river journey down the Thames to Oxford. Where was its author Jerome K. Jerome buried?

9 Well known woman novelist and a resident of the village of Finstock.

10 Flora Thompson's *Candleford* is no less real for having been an imaginary town based on an amalgamation of Bicester, Banbury and Buckingham. *Lark Rise* was a real place, but we know it by another name.

13 MILITARY MATTERS

War is much too serious a thing to be left to military men.

Attributed to Charles Maurice de Talleyrand and quoted by Briand to Lloyd George.

1 In the Civil War did Oxford side with the Royalists or the Parliamentarians?

2 Blenheim Palace was a token of the nation's gratitude to the Duke of Marlborough for his victory over the French at the Battle of Blenheim in 1704. Where is Blenheim?

3 This Oxford college was established for the purpose of providing masses for the souls of the fallen at the Battle of Agincourt in 1415.

4 The first major battle of the Civil War took place here in 1642.

5 Where can you see a stone war memorial with the figure l taken from the clock of the great Cloth Hall in Ypres which was destroyed by fighting in the Great War?

6 It is now a National Trust tea room, but in Cromwell's time it served as a mess room.

7 Memorial to a local hero where the surrounding trees were planted to record the battle lines at Alma in the Crimean War.

8 Home of the Royal Military College.

9 This is the site of Britain's largest operational RAF base.

10 The tomb of Henry Tudor's standard bearer at the Battle of Bosworth. The remains of the flag hang in the family chapel of this medieval manor house.

14 MISCELLANEOUS

Why is this thus?
What is the reason for this thusness?
Artemus Ward (Charles Farrar Brown). *Artemus Ward's Lecture.*

1 When did North Berkshire become South Oxfordshire?

2 It is fifty-six miles by road from Oxford to London. How many by river?

3 Name the seven towns of Otmoor.

4 Oxfordshire has boundaries with six other counties. Name them.

5 The massive cooling towers of Didcot Power Station are unmistakeable landmarks of modern Oxfordshire. How many are there?

6 In recent years the county council has created a network of cycle paths all over the county making it a paradise for cyclists. How many miles do they cover?

7 How many tourists visit Oxford annually?

8 What is the square mileage of the county.

9 Who wrote: 'To call a man an Oxford man is to pay him the highest compliment that can be paid to a human being'?

10 Who gave the following advice: 'Oxford is on the whole more attractive than Cambridge to the ordinary visitor; and the traveller is recommended to visit Cambridge first, or to omit it altogether if he cannot visit both'?

15 MUSEUMS

1 This Oxfordshire museum gives free entrance to people wearing seventeenth century style dress, otherwise adults pay one pound.

2 This one has among its bygones a collection of antique washing machines including one acquired by the Duke of Marlborough for Blenheim.

3 Included in the original inventory of this collection is an item: 'Dodar from the Island Mauritius; it is not able to flie, being so big'.

4 More of a farm than a museum. You can a milk a cow here.

5 Burford's fascinating town museum is housed in The Tolsey. What is a 'Tolsey'?

6 An enchanting riverside shrine to the Arts and Crafts Movement.

7 One of the most important ethnological museums in the world, but often referred to as 'Oxford's best kept secret'.

8 A museum documenting the history of the telephone. Does this ring a bell?

9 A collection of houses for very small people. Only dolls need apply.

10 Quizmaster Magnus Magnusson guides you along this multi-million pound ride through time.

16 MUSIC

Music' she said dreamily; and such is the force of habit that 'I don't' she added, 'know anything about music, really. But I know what I like.'

Max Beerbohm. *Zuleika Dobson.*

1 The college choir sings at dawn on May Day from the top of this tower.

2 Another tower – this time it is all that is left of St Martin's church at the Carfax. Which English composer was baptised in the church?

3 Where can you see the celebrated Stradivarius violin known as 'the Messiah'?

4 Once known for house parties and literary soirees, this place is now a known for opera.

5 Music was studied by medieval Oxford university students as part of the Quadrivium. What were the other three subjects?

6 Businessman Richard Branson set up a recording studios in the converted squash court of this country house. Virgin Records was the beginning of an empire.

7 The composer of the *The Beggar's Opera* stayed at Middleton Park near Bicester with his patron, the third Duke of Queensbury. The beautiful duchess, Lady Catherine, took a keen interest in his works. Swift wrote that he did not envy the composer 'for anything as much as being a domestic friend to such a lady'.

8 It is the first purpose-built concert venue in England and was opened in 1748.

9 Fireworks accompany the music at the popular summer concerts held at this famous public school.

10 Where can you see a fine stained glass window by Edward Burne-Jones dedicated to the patron saint of music?

17 PRE-HISTORY

We will now discuss in a little more detail the struggle for existence.
Charles Darwin. *The Origin of the Species.*

1 Lots of pre-historic bones have been dug up over the years in Oxfordshire – rhinos, hippos, mammoths and cave lions, but where might you see dinosaur bones?

2 What are known as the Whispering Knights and the King's Men?

3 This ancient road along the top of the downs is one of the oldest in the world.

4 The Uffington White Horse is not unique to the region. What county has the other six – and can you name all of them?

5 Who was the legendary occupant of Wayland's Smithy at Ashbury?

6 Various stretches of the massive earthworks known as Grim's Ditch or Devil's Dyke can still be seen. What is the legend relating to the structure?

7 Where is the Hawk Stone?

8 The Iron Age camp on the Sinodun Hills is sometimes called the Sinodun Clump. What else is the area called.

9 Name the earthworks, excavated by Pitt-Rivers in 1870, that were partly levelled some years later by a philanthropist intent on giving work to the local unemployed.

10 What legendary incident gave Dragon Hill at Uffington its name?

18 PUBS

HERESTO PANDS PEN D ASOCI
AL HOU R INHAR M (LES SMIRT)
HA ND FUNLET FRIENDS
HIPRE IGN BE JUSTAN DK
INDAN DEVIL SPEAKOF NO NE

1 Decipher the above sign hanging outside the Plough at East Hendred.

2 Inspector Morse unravels the final clue in *The Jewel that was Ours* while enjoying a pint here.

3 You will not need a tie in this Oxford pub. It houses a collection of more than 6,000 of them.

4 C S Lewis and his chums met here. Locals call it the Bird and Baby.

5 This ancient pub was once the town lock up and got its name from one of the felons housed there.

6 Cromwell celebrated here after the capture of Faringdon.

7 In the twelfth century this riverside pub, much favoured by fishermen, was a hospice for pilgrims to the nearby Godstow nunnery.

8 Thomas Hardy put this inn on the map in *Jude the Obscure*.

9 The landlady's son claimed William Shakespeare as his father. Whatever the truth of the matter, the bard attended the boy's christening at St Martin's church, right opposite this tavern.

10 Elizabeth I stayed here while hunting in Wychwood Forest.

19 RECORD BREAKERS

As the record from
youth to age
Of my own, the single
soul –
So the world's wide
book: one page
Deciphered explains the
whole
Of our common heritage.
Robert Burns. *Reverie.*

Where or what is:

1   Europe's oldest road.
2   Britain's smallest cathedral.
3   The oldest botannical garden.
4   The oldest legible tombstone.
5   Largest village in England.
6   Oldest woman – she died in 1718.
7   Oldest primary school.
8   England's first newspaper.
9   Biggest garden maze.
10 Oxford's smallest pub.

20 ROMANS

'Twas for the good of my country that I should be abroad. Anything for the good of one's country – I'm a Roman for that.
George Farquhar. *The Beaux Strategem.*

1 This tiny, isolated chapel is built on the site of a Roman villa.

2 It was known as Durocina in Roman times. Later this military station became a Saxon settlement.

3 Name the Roman road that crosses Oxfordshire from east to west.

4 Bicester may or may not have been Roman, but this nearby settlement certainly was.

5 Which native British tribe inhabited the region before the Roman invasion.

6 This village is named after a famous Roman general. He died in 516.

7 It is the best preserved of the county's Roman villas. It had sixty rooms, and was first excavated in 1815.

8 In what year did the Romans invade Britain?

9 And when did they leave?

10 Traces of what industry of the Roman occupation were revealed when the site of the Churchill Hospital at Headington was excavated?

21 ROYAL VISITORS

*George the First was always reckoned
Vile, but viler George the Second;
And what mortal ever heard
Any good of George the Third?
When from earth the Fourth descended
God be praised, the Georges ended!*

Walter Savage Landor. *Epigram*

1 This queen escaped from Oxford castle in the snow wearing a white robe to disguise herself as she crossed the frozen river.

2 Who was born in Beaumont Castle?

3 A yew was planted beside Rycote Chapel to mark his coronation – 800 years ago.

4 Who was the 'Winter Queen'?

5 Which king gave Oxford its first charter?

6 Queen's College was named after Queen Philippa, wife of which king?

7 But the likeness of another queen stands beneath the cupola on the college gatehouse. . .

8 This king was born in Islip.

9 This church has a lifesize statue of Elizabeth I, complete with crown, orb and sceptre.

10 Which king summoned the entire Court and Parliament to Oxford? Most of them came.

22 SCIENCE

Science is nothing but trained and organised common sense.
T H Huxley. *Collected Essays.*

1 Linacre College was founded in Oxford in 1962. Who was Linacre?

2 This fine scientific building was modelled on the Tower of the Winds in Athens.

3 A Savillian Professor of Astronomy better known for his work as an architect.

4 Another astronomer. A Franciscan with a reputation for dabbling in alchemy and the black arts, he carried out scientific experiments in a house on Folly Bridge.

5 Better known for the comet named after him, this scientist observed a strange spot on the sun in Oxford with a remarkable 24ft long telescope.

6 Where can you see Einstein's blackboard?

7 Eminent physician who came to Oxford with the court of King Charles. Allegedly he was deep in a book all through the Battle of Edgehill.

8 'The Father of British Geology'. He was born and buried in the village of Churchill.

9 A wonderful seventeenth century clock was made by Hercules Hastings for the tower of this church.

10 Inventor of the famous 'powders' which cured everthing. The recipe was a well kept secret but is said to have included grass cuttings from the garden of his uncle's house at Kidlington.

23 SPORT

And so too have I paused and held my oar
And suffered the slow stream to bear me home
While Wykeham's peal along the meadow ran.
James Hurdis. *The Village Curate.*

1 The historic year in which Roger Bannister broke the four minute mile at Oxford University Sports Ground at Iffley Road.

2 The sport of princes if not of kings? What is played at Kirtlington Park?

3 Oxfordshire's own Aunt Sally League is as fiercely contested as any sport. But what is the game?

4 How does the technique of an Oxford punter differ from a Cambridge punter?

5 International Horse Trials held each September in palatial setting?

6 Henley's world famous rowing club.

7 The 1997 World Pooh Sticks Championship held here was called off when the river froze over.

8 What are the 'Torpids'?

9 Croquet as played by the Red Queen in Lewis Carroll's *Alice in Wonderland* had some strange rules. What did they use for mallets and balls.

10 Name the flamboyant businessman who fell off his yacht. He was also the high-profile ex-proprietor of Oxford Football Club.

24 STONE

City of weathered cloister and worn court;
Gray city of strong towers and clustering spires:
Where art's first loveliness would first resort;
Where lingering art kindled her latest fires.

Lionel Johnson. *Oxford.*

1 What gives the stone of the Banbury area its rich ochre colour?

2 Burford church has a moving and exquisitely carved memorial to one of the greatest of stone carvers, Christopher Kempster who died in 1715. What building was his crowning achievement?

3 Name his best known work in Oxfordshire.

4 The county's buildings use many materials. Bicester is mainly built of clay and local brick. Cotswold villages are renowned for their golden limestone. But what are Chiltern villages built from?

5 Stone by name, stone by trade. Another famous Oxfordshire mason.

6 What is 'clunch'?

7 Cambridge is mostly built of brick. Where did Oxford's fine ashlar stone come from?

8 Sir Christopher Wren is buried here.

9 Oolitic limestone is a more formal name for the distinctive Cotswold stone. What does 'oolitic' mean?

10 To which counties does the Four Shires Stone point?

25 THE THAMES

1 Where might you come across an impressive riverside statue of Old Father Thames?

2 Give the number of miles that the River Thames flows through Oxfordshire.

3 And the number of locks on the Thames.

4 Oxford is the meeting place of which two rivers.

5 Hospitality tents almost outnumber picnic hampers for Henley Royal Regatta in the first week of July each year. When was the first regatta held?

6 This oddly named island is the traditional starting point for the races.

7 Oxford itself grew up as a safe gravel bedded ford over the Thames. This village further downstream began life as a river crossing for the Icknield Way.

8 What is the length of the great river bridge at Wallingford.

9 Police come out in force to stop exuberant students from jumping off this bridge in May.

10 Who was the famous engineer who built the railway bridge over the Thames at Moulsford.

26 TRANSPORT

*You will hear more good things
on the outside of a stagecoach
from London to Oxford than if
you were to pass a twelvemonth
with the undergraduates, or
heads of colleges, of that
famous university.*

William Hazlitt. *Table Talk*

1 How many hours did it take to reach London by Oxford's latest high-speed 'flying coach' – in 1669?

2 What make of car does Inspector Morse drive?

3 The foot-weary can jump aboard a narrow gauge model railway to tour the grounds of this palatial residence.

4 This car manufacturer endowed a Centre for Japanese Studies at Oxford University.

5 MG sports cars were built here until 1980.

6 Mecca for railway enthusiasts. Here they can potter about in the engine sheds and examine the rolling stock and original broad gauge track of the Great Western Railway.

7 This 65-acre park contains the largest collection of British cars in the world.

8 Name Oxfordshire's last two remaining toll bridges.

9 This village churchyard has a strange memorial to Sir Benjamin Baker who designed the London Underground system, the Aswan Dam and the railway bridge across the Firth of Forth.

10 Here there is a fabulous collection of model railways in realistic settings.

27 UNIVERSITY

*Oxford for eels, Cambridge
for schools.*
Old saying.

1 How many Oxford colleges are there?

2 Name the three academic terms.

3 Cambridge colleges have masters. Oxford
college masters boast a variety of impressive
titles . . .

4 This college produced an astonishing total of
fourteen British Prime Ministers.

5 Who was Great Tom – the Christ Church bell which rings 101 times at
nine each night – named after. And why does it ring 101 times?

6 St Scholastica's day in 1355 was a black day for the university. What
happened?

7 The three oldest Oxford colleges.

8 What is *sub fusc*?

9 Who wrote of his university lodgings: 'The floors are in general laid with
white clay and covered with rushes, occasionally removed, but so
imperfectly that the bottom layer is left undisturbed, sometimes for
twenty years, harbouring expectorations, vomitings, the leakage of dogs
and men, ale-droppings, scraps of fish and other abominations not fit
to be mentioned . . .'?

10 John Major did not go to university but Tony Blair did. Where?

28 WOOL

The sheep sometime did tread the maze
By often wynding in and in,
And sometymes round about they trace
Which milkmayds call a Fairie ring.
William Strode. *On Westwell Downs.*

1 This Cotswold town – world famous for its blankets – has a fine Blanket Hall built by weavers in 1721.

2 Unusual 'bale' tombs figure prominently in Burford churchyard. What are they thought to represent.

3 This fine woollen mill, described as 'a cross between St. Pancras Station and Balmoral castle', was turned into luxury flats in 1980.

4 This working farm has a permanent exhibition on the blanket making industry of Witney and a resident blanket maker who demonstrates his art.

5 Woodstock's traditional industry was a by-product of the long-established woollen industry. It was?

6 Name the three great 'wool' churches of the Oxfordshire Cotswolds.

7 Wool was weighed in 'tods'. How much did a tod weigh?

8 What were Cotswold Lions?

9 Witney escaped the fate of other North Cotswold woollen centres which suffered a disastrous decline in the seventeenth century. What was the reason for its success and survival?

10 Wool for export had to pass through one English port – its merchants formed a 'staple', deals were done and huge revenues collected for the British crown. Which port?

PICTURE QUIZ – THE VILLAGES

1 This was the village school described in detail by Thomas Hughes in *Tom Brown's Schooldays*. Today it is used for another purpose. What is it?

2 An unorthodox type of building material decorates the wall of this barn at Harpsden Court Farm. What are these blocks?

3   Where is this magnificent New Stone Age burial chamber and whose name does it bear?

4   This is The Cottage at Juniper Hill. It bears a commemorative plaque to the writer who lived there as a child. Whose name appears on it?

5 This building, which belongs to the National Trust, is the largest of its kind in the country. What is it and where is it?

6 What is this and what is its literary connection?

7 On which buildings in which Oxfordshire village does this carving by George Jack appear?

8 One of the finest medieval tombs in England is in the church of St Mary the Virgin at Ewelme. Who lies within it?

9 A puzzle picture. In what building can be seen this fine example of medieval craftsmanship?

10 This is the Grand Bridge at Blenheim. Its architect declared that he was determined to build 'the finest bridge in Europe'. Who was he?

PICTURE QUIZ – THE TOWNS

1 There are thirty two canvas panels on the ceiling of this theatre designed by Christopher Wren. Who painted them?

2 What and where is this town centre structure?

3 Only the thirteenth century tower, with this splendid clock, remains of the church that stood at Oxford's busy crossroads. To whom was the church dedicated?

4 What is this and of what Oxford college is it an architectural feature?

5 To what in Oxford is this handsome gateway the entrance?

6 This island is the starting point for the Henley Royal Regatta races.
   Who was architect who designed the neo-Classical temple on it in 1771?

7 Banbury's present day cross was built to mark a royal wedding
in 1858. Who was the bride?

8 A great man who added considerably to the wealth of human knowledge
lived and worked in this house in the eighteenth century. Who was he?

9 Whose face is this? And where is the bridge?

10 From what does the Tower of the Five Orders opposite the Bodleian Library take its name?

ANSWERS

1 ALFRED

1 Wessex and Mercia.
2 Wantage, in 849 AD.
3 The sarsen stone has a hole at the top which, when blown like a trumpet, emits an enormously impressive loud note. Legend has it that Alfred summoned his troops for battle by blowing on this giant piece of Ice Age debris.
4 The so called 'Alfred Jewel' was found near Athelney in Somerset where King Alfred had spent the winter of 878 AD in hiding.
5 War hero and local landowner Lord Wantage, better known as Colonel Robert Loyd-Lindsay, first holder of the Victoria Cross for his bravery in the Crimean War. He also paid for the statue. The cost was 2,000 guineas.
6 Queen Victoria's nephew Count Heinrich Ludwig von Gleichen-Russworn.
7 This picturesque spring by Letcombe Brook in Wantage may well have had something to do with the king. But more likely it was named after Alfred Hazell, a cloth maker who lived at the nearby Mead.
8 An Iron Age hill fort on White Horse Hill, on the other side of the B4000 to Lambourne. Alfred may well have used these earlier fortifications.
9 The Battle of Ashdown.
10 Faringdon. Alfred's son, Edward the Elder, died here in 924.

2 ALICE

1 Christ Church. The library in Peckwater Quad has an interesting collection of Carroll memorabilia.
2 Alice Liddell, ten year old daughter af the Dean af Christ Church. Her sisters were called Lorina and Edith.
3 Charles Lutwidge Dodgson. His pseudonym was formed by Latinising his names, reversing their order and then translating them back into English. Dodgson hid behind his pseudonym and never publicly acknowledged the authorship of his children's stories.
4 Two afternoons a week Lord Harcourt opened the grounds of his riverside mansion, Nuneham Park, to the public. Dodgson and the Liddell party rowed there for picnic teas. The Thursday outing was rained off, and as the house was closed on Fridays, Dodgson rowed the girls and their chaperones down to Godstow the following day (4 July 1862). It was on this occasion that he started telling the story of Alice's adventures.
5 The boating party had heen soaked to the skïn in torrential rain on the river two weeks previously.
6 A shop in a fifteenth century building on the south side of St Aldates.

7 The view from Beckley acress Otmoor.
8 *A Syllabus of Plane Alegebraic Geometry.*
9 John Tenniell, the talented *Punch* cartoonist.
10 *Alice's Adventures Under Ground.*

3 ALL CREATURES GREAT AND SMALL

1 The Cotswold Wild Life Park, near Burford. No other sightings have been reported.
2 Rousham House near Deddington. William Kent designed the glorious gardens.
3 Otmoor. The Riot Act was read in 1830 and forty-one people were carted off to Oxford jail, only to be freed by a mob later. More recently, local opinion has stopped the M40 from being routed through the moor.
4 Water was pulled up from the well at Grey's Court near Henley by donkeys until 1914. The fortified medieval manor house, which is owned by the National Trust, was the home of the Knollys family.
5 The pavement outside Stiles Almshouses in Wantage is made from the knucklebones of sheep. Presumably this was a case of using whatever came to hand. There were plenty of sheep on the downs and possibly the bones may have been a byproduct of the glove industry.
6 Long Wittenham Nature Reserve, near Wallingford.
7 Minster Lovell Manor in the Windrush valley, near Burford.
8 In Chipping Norton cemetery. Davey Barnard died in 1973, aged forty-eight.
9 A worm. (Latin)
10 The Boarstall Duck Decoy and Nature Reserve, near Brill.

4 ARTS AND CRAFTS

1 William Morris's summer home, Kelmscott Manor, on the Thames near Faringdon.
2 John Ruskin. A plaque on the wall of one of the cottages in the village commemorates the project in the summer of 1874.
3 Edward Burne-Jones, a frequent guest of William Morris at nearby Kelmscott, completed the fairytale series for the first Lord Faringdon in 1890.
4 The church of Sts Peter and Paul at Checkendon. Eric Kennington was a sculptor, artist and a friend of Lawrence of Arabia.
5 The Chiltern Sculpture Trail in Cowleaze Wood at Christmas Common.
6 William Morris, Edward Burne-Jones and Dante Gabriel Rossetti decorated the Debating Chamber of the Oxford Union building on St Michael's Street. The themes of the paintings were taken from the legends of King Arthur.

7 In the Latin Chapel of Christ Church Cathedral, Oxford. Burne-Jones completed this work in 1858, when he was twenty-five.
8 Chipping Norton Theatre, famous for its Christmas pantomimes and its innovative cultural programmes.
9 Sculptor Eric Gill.
10 The thirteenth century tithe barn at Great Coxwell. It is 152ft long, 44ft wide and 48ft high at the ridge.

5 CHURCHES

1 Banbury's Gothic church had suffered considerable damage during the Civil War.
2 St Mary's, Swinbrook in the Windrush valley.
3 Garsington.
4 Corinthian pilasters adorn the Georgian front of Burford's Methodist church which was built in the eighteenth century as the town house of a local lawyer.
5 St Peter's, near the manor house at Stanton Harcourt.
6 St Mary's, Thame.
7 Rycote, built by Sir John Williams, guardian of the young Elizabeth I who often visited him there. As did James I and Charles I, for whom the royal pew was installed in 1625 when an outbreak of plague forced Parliament and the Court to move to Oxford.
8 Each year Levellers Day is celebrated at Burford churchyard with eminent speakers reflecting a wide political spectrum.
9 St Mary the Virgin, Black Bourton. Medieval wall paintings were whitewashed over during the Reformation, and generally only came to light in Victorian times when churches underwent a thorough restoration.
10 The early fourteenth century Tree of Jesse window in Dorchester Abbey.

6 COUNTRY HOUSES

1 Blenheim Palace, built between 1705 and 1722 for the Duke of Marlborough at a cost of more than £500,000 after his victory over the Dutch at the Battle of Blenheim.
2 George Washington. It is said that the family coat of arms was the inspiration for the US flag, the Stars and Stripes. Sulgrave is just over the Oxfordshire border – in Northamptonshire.
3 Ditchley Park, near Charlbury, designed by James Gibb in 1722 now an Anglo-American conference centre.
4 Mapledurham House, near Caversham, was Kenneth Grahame's model for Toad Hall.

5 An imperial staircase starts off as twin flights of stairs at the base, merging into a single staircase on the upper floors.
6 National Trust-owned Chastleton House was built between 1603 amnd 1618 on land belonging to Robert Catesby, leading conspirator of the Gunpowder Plot. He was forced to sell his estate to pay a huge fine imposed on him by Queen Elizabeth I for supporting the Earl of Essex.
7 Minster Lovell Hall, near Burford, which was begun in 1431 by William Lovell on his return from the wars in France. A skeleton found sitting at a table in an underground room, discovered in 1728, may have been his grandson Francis, who went into hiding after the Battle of Stoke.
8 Stonor, near Henley, home of Lord and Lady Camoys and the Stonor family. Part of the house dates from 1190.
9 Broughton Castle, near Banbury, acquired by the second Lord Saye and Sele in 1451. James I slept there in 1604.
10 Ashdown House, reputedly built in 1660 by the Earl of Craven as a refuge for Elizabeth, the 'Winter Queen', daughter of James I. She died of plague in London before the house was finished.

7 ECCENTRICS

1 Clough William Ellis lived in the beautiful manor house at Cornwall, near Chipping Norton. He created the fantasy village of Portmeiron in the 1930s but luckily he ran out of ideas for improving his surroundings and Cornwall remains quite unspoilt.
2 A garden pavilion at his stately home, Buscot Park near Faringdon, where he lavishly entertained leading members of the Labour Party in the 1930s and 1940s. The bizarre murals were executed by a friend, Lord Hastings, who had studied with the fashionable Mexican socialist painter, Diego Rivera.
3 Unity Mitford, sister of writers Nancy and Jessica, who married Sir Oswald Mosley, leader of the British Fascist Party and ardent admirer of Adolf Hitler.
4 The 15th Lord Saye and Sele, profligate and notorious owner of Broughton Castle. He ended up – in 1837 – selling everything, even the swans on the moat.
5 He seems to have collected names, too – Lieutenant General Augustus Henry Lane Fox Pitt Rivers.
6 1n 1794 young poet Walter Savage Landor left in disgrace after firing a pistol out his quadrangle window at a passing Tory. He missed.
7 Lord Berner's impressive folly near Faringdon built in 1935. At the foot of the tower he erected a notice which read: 'Members of the public committing suicide from this tower do so at their own risk'.

8 Car manufacturer and multi-millionaire, William Morris, later Lord Nuffield.

9 John Falkner, who died at Appleford, near Abingdon, in 1933 at the age of 104.

10 Middle Aston. The church at neighbouring Steeple Aston has a chilling life-size memorial to Justice Page.

8 FAMOUS MEN AND WOMAN

1 Sir Winston Churchill.

2 Mary Somerville.

3 St Frideswide.

4 Lord Asquith – Prime Minister from 1908-1916.

5 Thomas Cranmer, Archbishop of Canterbury, Nicholas Ridley, Bishop of London, and Hugh Latimer, Bishop of Worcester, tried for heresy, were burned at the stake in 1555 and 1556.

6 United States President, Bill Clinton, Rhodes Scholar at University College. While at Oxford Clinton lodged at 46 Leckford Road.

7 William Morris – and William Morris.

8 Mistress of Henry II, educated at Godstow Abbey, and buried after her death at Woodstock.

9 William Spooner, inventor of the Spoonerism.

10 Dr Sewell. 1847.

9 FILM LOCATIONS

1 *Brideshead Revisited*. Filmed at Waugh's alma mater, Hertford College, with its picturesque Bridge of Sighs.

2 Sir Richard Attenborough's 1994 film *Shadowlands* starring Anthony Hopkins and Debra Winger.

3 Blenheim Palace, near Woodstock.

4 *Howard's End*.

5 Actor Nigel Hawthorne.

6 *A Fish Called Wanda*

7 Colin Dexter's Inspector Morse.

8 Garsington Manor, former home of socialite Lady Ottoline Morrell, and now an idyllic setting for a summer opera festival.

9 Broughton Castle, near Banbury.

10 Hambledon.

10 FOOD AND DRINK

1 Scott of the Antarctic took a tin of Oxford Marmalade with him to the South Pole. It is preserved at the Museum of Oxford.
2 Stanton Harcourt Manor House has an immense beamed medieval kitchen with an octagonal beamed roof with wooden louvres to let out the smoke from the open fireplace and ovens.
3 The royal bun fight took place at Abingdon.
4 The rustic Butter Cross at Witney, topped by a cupola and clock turret, was the site of the town's busy market.
5 Hook Norton's famous brew, Old Hookey, was produced in the town's semi-gravitational tower brewery, built in 1900 by the son of maltster John Harris who founded the brewery in 1856.
6 The holy well in Binsey village churchyard provided the inspiration for the Treacle Well in Lewis Carroll's *Alice in Wonderland*.
7 Raymond Blanc's famous Oxfordshire restaurant, Le Manoir aux Quat' Saisons at Great Milton, with its two Michelin stars.
8 Aristotle. It is not known which of the philosopher's works stopped the boar.
9 Watercress. In the nineteenth century villages like Ewelme made a lively profit sending watercress to London for sale..
10 Venison from the royal forest was invariably poached, and always on the menu in Wychwood inns.

11 GARDENS

1 Henry Danvers, Lord Danby, founded the Oxford Botanic Garden as part of the School of Medecine. The original three acre walled physick garden was laid out in 1630.
2 The Ashmolean Museum. Tradescant's son gave the rarities to Elias Ashmole, Windsor Herald.
3 Greys Court, near Henley-on-Thames.
4 The Anglo-American Garden is at Dorchester Abbey. It was founded by a Boston woman, Edith Stedman.
5 Lord Faringdon's house, Buscot Park.
6 'Capability' Brown in the late eighteenth century.
7 Nuneham Courtenay. The fifty five acre park was laid out in 1835 and is now managed by Oxford University which use the great house, Nuneham Park, as a conference centre.
8 The marvellous gardens at Rousham House were laid out by William Kent between 1738 and 1740.

9 Waterperry Horticultural Centre started by Miss Beatrix Havergal and six students.

10 At Kingston Lisle Park near Wantage. The original is, of course, in London's Regents's Park.

12 LITERARY LIVES

1 Max Beerbohm. Merton College has a two roomed exhibition dedicated to the writer who left Oxford in 1894 without taking his exams.

2 The poet was a guest at Stanton Harcourt Manor House.

3 The Mitford children spent much of their childhood at Swinbrook in the Windrush valley. Nancy and Unity are buried in the churchyard.

4 The Newdigate Poetry Prize, awarded for a poem on a set theme.

5 Thomas Hughes, born in Uffington in 1822, author of *Tom Brown's Schooldays*.

6 Poet Sir John Betjeman.

7 Matthew Arnold, whose favourite view of Oxford was from Boar's Hill. The archeologist Sir Arthur Evans made a gift of land on the wooded hillside and named it Matthew Arnold's Field.

8 The churchyard of Ewelme. He died in 1927.

9 Barbara Pym.

10 Flora Thompson immortalised, but renamed, the tiny hamlet of Juniper Hill, where she was born during a snow storm in 1876, in her trilogy *Lark Rise to Candleford*.

13 MILITARY MATTERS

1 Oxford was the headquarters of the Royalists during the Civil War.

2 Blenheim, now Blindheim, on the River Danube.

3 The College of all the Souls of the Faithful Departed – better known as All Souls.

4 The Battle of Edge Hill. Charles I led the Royalist troops against the army of Parliament commanded by Robert Devereaux, third Earl of Essex.

5 On the village green at Westwell, near Burford.

6 The old stables at Greys Court, near Henley.

7 The monument to Lord Wantage, near the Ridgeway on the B4494.

8 Shrivenham.

9 Brize Norton.

10 Sir Robert Harcourt of Stanton Harcourt Manor. The battle took place in 1485.

14 MISCELLANEOUS

1 After the boundary changes of 1974.
2 Twice as far – 112 miles.
3 Beckley, Charlton, Fencot, Horton, Murcot, Noke and Oddington.
4 Northamptonshire, Buckinghamshire, Berkshire, Wiltshire, Gloucestershire and Warwickshire.
5 Six.
6 An astonishing, but ecologically correct, 220 miles.
7 Nearly two million.
8 1,008 square miles (2,611 square kilometers).
9 Christ Church graduate (in 1831) and Prime Minister, William Gladstone.
10 Karl Baedecker, German publisher of the famous series of guidebooks. In his volume on Great Britain published in 1887.

15 MUSEUMS

1 The Edge Hill Battle Museum at Farnborough Hall, near Banbury.
2 The Claydon Granary Museum of Bygones.
3 John Tradescant brought the now extinct specimen back from a plant hunting expedition. His collection of natural history curiosities was dubbed Tradescant's Ark. His collection formed the basis for Oxford's Ashmolean Museum.
4 Cogges Manor Farm Museum. near Witney.
5 Traders in Burford's busy market paid their tolls here.
6 Kelmscott Manor has the finest collection of Arts and Crafts Movement furnishings designed by William Morris – all in their original setting.
7 The Pitt Rivers Museum in Parks Road, Oxford.
8 The Telecom Museum in Speedwell Street, Oxford.
9 The Rotunda Museum of Antique Dolls Houses at Grove House, Iffley Turn, Oxford.
10 The award-winning *Oxford Story* – a high-tech history of the city.

16 MUSIC

1 Magdalen College Tower.
2 Orlando Gibbons. He was appointed organist of the Chapel Royal in 1604 and of Westminster Abbey in 1623. The church was demolished in 1896.
3 In the Hill Music Room of the Ashmolean Museum. The violin dates from 1716.

4 Garsington Manor, which holds an annual Opera Festival each June. A previous lady of the manor was Lady Ottoline Morrell who entertained literary lions such as D H Lawrence, Bertrand Russell, Virginia Woolf and T S Eliot. The atmosphere of the house and the eccentricity of its hostess are recreated in Lawrence's novel, *Women in Love.*

5 Arithmetic, geometry and astronomy. They also had to study grammar, rhetoric and logic which formed the Trivium. Seven years of study.

6 The fifteenth century manor house at Shipton-on-Cherwell near Kidlington, bought by Richard Branson in 1971, became one of the most famous pop recording studios in England. Mike Oldfield's *Tubular Bells* was one of its first hits.

7 John Gay. He had lost all his money in the South Sea Bubble.

8 The Holywell Music Room. George IV gave the chandeliers.

9 Radley College.

10 The Saint Cecilia window is in the north choir aisle of Christ Church Cathedral, Oxford.

17 PRE-HISTORY

1 At the University Museum in Parks Road.

2 The Rollright Stones. Many legends have been woven around this prehistoric stone circle, and the groups of stones have their names. The seventey-seven stones which form the circle are known as the King's Men. Five nearby stones are called the Whispering Knights and a large monolith is called the King.

3 The 85-mile Icknield Way or Ridgeway, probably 5,000 years old.

4 All in neighbouring Wiltshire, but none as old as the Uffington horse. They are at Pewsey, cut in 1937; Alton Barnes, 1812; at Bratton near Westbury, 1778; Oldbury Castle, 1780; Hackpen Hill, 1838; and at Marlborough, 1804.

5 A legendary Saxon blacksmith, known as Weland or Wayland. He would, it was said, shoe the horses of people who left a silver coin at his door and tethered their beasts nearby.

6 It was thought that Old Nick ploughed the great ditch in one long night, casting his scrapings into heaps which were later found to be ancient round barrows.

7 At the village of Chadlington. It is eight feet high.

8 Wittenham Clumps. Near Dorchester-on-Thames.

9 The Dyke Hills or Dorchester Earthworks.

10 It was here, according to tradition, that St George slew the dragon. The bare patch is caused by the dragon's blood.

18 PUBS

1 Here stop and spend a social hour in harmless mirth and fun.
   Let friendship reign. Be just and kind and evil speak of none.
2 The Kings Arms in Parks Road.
3 The Bear in Alfred Street.
4 The Eagle and Child.
5 The Bird Cage Inn at Thame which dates from 1430. The highwayman in
   question was nicknamed the Magpie. Locals, referring to his capture, supposedly
   said: The bird is in his cage'.
6 The Bell Inn, Faringdon.
7 The Trout Inn, Lower Wolvercote. The earliest part dates from 1133.
8 The Turf Tavern, in Bath Place, next to the old city wall.
9 William Davenant's mother ran the Crown Tavern, a gabled building at 3
   Cornmarket Street, near Carfax. John Aubrey records that Shakespeare
   stayed at the Crown every year on his way back to Stratford-upon-Avon.
10 The Shaven Crown at Shipton-under-Wychwood.

19 RECORD BREAKERS

1 The Ridgeway. This eighty-five mile long track runs along the chalk downland
   ridge above the Thames valley.
2 Christ Church Cathedral, founded in 1546 as the college chapel.
3 Oxford Botanical Garden, founded in 1621.
4 The churchyard at Upton has a tombstone to the memory of a John Brooker,
   clearly bearing the burial date of 1551.
5 Kidlington, population 17,000, where residents voted not to become a town.
6 Elizabeth Bowles of West Hannay who lived to be an amazing – and unlikely –
   124 years of age. Her tomb is in the churchyard.
7 Ewelme village has the oldest church primary school in the country. It dates
   from 1437.
8 The *Oxford Gazette*, published by the Oxford University printing press in 1665,
   when the court of Charles I was at Oxford.
9 The Marlborough Maze at Blenheim Palace – opened in 1991, the Year of the
   Maze.
10 The Bear in Alfred Street. It reputedly dates back to 1242.

20 ROMANS

1. A Roman mosaic pavement forms part of the floor of St. Oswald's at Widford, near Burford.
2. Dorchester-on-Thames.
3. Akeman Street. It connects Watling Street with the Fosse Way.
4. Alchester – Roman camp on the road across Otmoor to Dorchester.
5. The Dobunni.
6. Ambroseden, near Bicester, named after Ambrosius Aurelianus, the last of the Roman military commanders to take a stand against the Anglo-Saxons in the twilight years of the Roman Empire.
7. North Leigh Roman villa, near Witney.
8. In the summer of AD 43 Aulus Plautius' expeditionary force landed on the south coast of Britain.
9. In 410. Following the sack of Rome by Alaric the Goth the Emperor Honorius told the Britons to arrange for their own defence.
10. Production of colour-coated fine pottery. Several third century kilns were excavated on the hospital site.

21 ROYAL VISITORS

1. Queen Matilda, who after being beseiged in the castle for ten weeks in 1141, managed to escape to refuge in Abingdon.
2. Richard Coeur de Lion in 1157. He was the son of Henry II and Eleanor of Aquitaine.
3. King Stephen in 1135.
4. Elizabeth, daughter of James I, sister of Charles I and wife of the Elector of Palatine. William, Earl of Craven, built Ashdown House for her, but she died of plague in London before she saw it. Some historians think that she may have secretly married the earl.
5. Henry II, in 1155.
6. Edward III. The college was founded in 1341 by her chaplain, Robert Eglesfield.
7. Queen Caroline, wife of George II. The statue, by Henry Cheere, was erected in 1734.
8. Edward the Confessor, in 1004. An interesting portrait hangs in the church.
9. St Michael's, Cumnor. The queen's favourite, the Earl of Leicester, lived at Cumnor Place with his wife Amy Robsart, who was mysteriously found dead at the bottom of a flight of stairs.

10 Charles I in January 1644, during the Civil War. The king addressed them in Christ Church. The Commons then convened in the Divinity School and the House of Lords in the university's Convocation House.

22 SCIENCE

1 Thomas Linacre came to Oxford as a Fellow of All Soul's after studying medicine at the University of Padua. He was a friend of Erasmus and Thomas More and founded the College of Physicians in 1518.
2 The Radcliffe Observatory, built by James Wyatt in 1772-94.
3 Sir Christopher Wren. The young professor was simultaneously working on designs for the classical Sheldonian Theatre, planned as the university's first great Assembly Room for academic ceremonies.
4 Roger Bacon.
5 Edmund Halley, who was appointed Astronomer Royal in 1720. He lived at 7 New College Lane and he predicted the appearance of the great comet of 1758, which became known as Halley's Comet, and its later appearances.
6 In the Museum of the History of Science, in Broad Street, Oxford.
7 Sir William Harvey (1578–1657) who discovered the circulation of the blood.
8 Burford. The mechanism worked perfectly for more than 300 years until replaced in 1940. The original clock can still be seen in the church which first mentions the clock in its accounts for the year 1625.
9 William Smith (1769–1839), author of the *New Geological Atlas of England and Wales*. A memorial stands on the village green.
10 Victorian pharmacist Thomas Beecham.

23 SPORT

1 In 1954
2 Polo. Prince Charles often plays here.
3 Aunt Sally – an Oxfordshire invention – is played in pubs throughout the county, the object being to knock a 'doll' off its stand by throwing sticks at it.
4 Oxford punters punt from the sloping end of the craft, Cambridge punters from the flat.
5 The Blenheim Palace International Horse Trials featuring show jumping and cross country.
6 The Leander Club.

7 The annual competition inspired by the antics of A P Herbert's *Winnie the Pooh* and attended by contestants from all over the world, is held on the River Thames at Long Wittenham on the first Sunday in January.
8 College rowing races held in February for less expert oarsmen.
9 Flamingoes and hedgehogs.
10 Robert Maxwell, who lived at Headington Hall.

24 STONE

1 Iron oxide.
2 St Paul's Cathedral. Kempster was Sir Christopher Wren's chief mason.
3 The Town Hall at Abingdon.
4 Flint and brick.
5 Seventeenth century mason Nicholas Stone, who built the imposing gate to Oxford's Botanic Garden, and John Dunne's tomb in St Paul's.
6. Black marble.
7 The quarries at Headington. It is a soft stone, easy to carve but quick to crumble.
8 Kirtlington.
9 Egglike. Under a microscope the fine grain of the stone looks like fish eggs.
10 The stone near Moreton-on-the-Marsh points to Gloucestershire, Warwickshire, Worcestershire and, of course, Oxfordshire.

25 THE THAMES

1 The huge statue which came from the Great Exhibition at Crystal Palace now sits by the river at St John's Lock, near Lechlade.
2 Seventy-eight miles.
3 Forty-five locks.
4 The rivers Thames or Isis and Cherwell.
5 In 1839. The regatta acquired the patronage of the Prince Consort in 1851.
6 Temple Island. The neo-classical temple was built by James Wyatt as the summerhouse of nearby Fawley Court. It was leased to the regatta in 1987.
7 Goring-on-Thames.
8 An astonishing 900 feet. It has been rebuilt many times.
9 Folly Bridge at Oxford.
10 Isambard Kingdom Brunel.

26 TRANSPORT

1 Thirteen hours. Today, little more than an hour.
2 A red Jaguar.
3 Blenheim Palace. The railway takes visitors from the house to the playground.
4 The Nissan Company of Japan – at St. Anthony's College.
5 Abingdon.
6 Didcot Railway Centre.
7 The £8million Heritage Motor Centre at Gaydon.
8 Whitchurch and Swinford.
9 Idbury, near Burford.
10 The Pendon Museum at Long Wittenham.

27 UNIVERSITY

1 Thirty six, of which eight colleges are for graduates only.
2 Michaelmas, Hilary and Trinity.
3 Warden, Principal, Provost, Rector, Dean or President.
4 Christ Church.
5 Thomas Wolsey, founder of the original college before Henry VIII became involved in university politics. There were originally 101 students who had to be in before curfew each night.
6 Riots between town and gown led to a number of deaths. The streets ran with blood but the town won.
7 Merton in 1264; University College in 1249; and Balliol in 1263.
8 The regulation dark suit, white shirt and white bow tie worn by examination students and for matriculation and degree ceremonies. Women are required to wear a dark skirt, white shirt and dark stockings.
9 The Renaissance scholar, Erasmus of Rotterdam, who came to Oxford in 1499.
10 St John's College.

28 WOOL

1 Witney. Blankets were brought here to be weighed and graded. More than 100,000 workers were employed in the industry here at the height of its prosperity in the eighteenth century.
2 Wool merchants tombs were given distinctive hooped lids in the seventeenth and early eighteenth century. They resembled the bales of wool on which the town's wealth was built and were beautifully decorated with cherubs and swags of flowers.

3 The Bliss Mill at Chipping Norton, built in 1873.

4 Cogges Manor Farm Museum at Cogges, near Witney.

5 Glovemaking.

6 Burford, Witney and Chipping Norton – all glorious testimony to the wealth of the area at the height of the woollen industry in the fifteenth century. Banbury's great church was demolished and rebuilt at the end of the eighteenth century.

7 28 lbs.

8 Large white Cotswold sheep, now a rare breed. They are distinguished by their abundant fleeces and curly forelocks.

9 The abundant and crystal clear waters of the River Windrush which flowed through the town and powered its mills. It escaped the fate of other North Cotswold towns, which saw their industries decline and moved towards the valleys of the Stroud area of Gloucestershire with their vital fast flowing streams.

10 Calais, now French, but an English port for centuries.

29 PICTURE QUIZ – VILLAGES

1 The Tom Brown's Schooldays Museum at Uffington. It is filled with relics of village life and the rules of the school are still on the wall.

2 Hand-carved wallpaper pattern blocks bought by John Noble of Park Place, Remenham. in the 1890s from a London printing works to line the walls of his boathouse. He died before the work was done.

3 On the Ridgeway at Ashbury. The Saxons named the tomb after Wayland, one of their gods who was a skilled metalworker.

4 Flora Thompson, author of *Lark Rise to Candleford*.

5 The greatest medieval tithe barn in England at Great Coxwell, Faringdon.

6 St Margaret's Well at Binsey. Holy medicinal springs like this one were known as 'treacle wells' in medieval Oxfordshire and this one is mentioned by Lewis Carroll in *Alice's Adventures in Wonderland*.

7 The 'William Morris muses in his garden' carving is on the Memorial Cottages in Kelmscott village.

8 Thomas Chaucer, son of the Geoffrey *'Canterbury Tales'* Chaucer, and his wife Matilda.

9 The manorial dovecote at Minster Lovell. It has been restored by English Heritage and is open daily, between 2pm and 5pm, from Easter to October.

10 Sir John Vanbrugh.

30 PICTURE QUIZ – TOWNS

1 Ralph Streeter, sergeant painter to Charles I.
2 The Butter Cross at Witney.
3 St Martin.
4 It is the open-air stone pulpit at Magdalene College.
5 The Botanic Garden in The High. It was built in 1632 Nicholas Stone.
6 James Wyatt, as a summerhouse for Sambrooke Freeman of Fawley Court.
7 Queen Victoria's eldest daughter, Victoria, married the German Emperor Frederick III.
8 Sir Edmund Halley who predicted the appearance of the comet that now bears his name.
9 The goddess Isis on the bridge built of Headington stone at a cost of £10,000 across the Thames at Henley.
10 From the five styles of classical colums – Tuscan, Doric, Ionic, Corinthian and Composite.

Front cover: It is one of the few surviving kilns in the county used in the manufacture of bricks and tiles. It is at Nettlebed, a centre of that industry from the Middle Ages.
Title page: The village lock up at Wheatley.
Back cover: Hercules Hastings was the maker of this clock, which is in Burford parish church.

ACKNOWLEDGEMENTS

The photographs for the picture quiz have been kindly provided by Edward Gill, author of *Curiosities of Oxfordshire,* published by S. B. Publications in 1995.

LINE DRAWINGS ON SPECIFIC SUBJECTS